Reasons To Believe   Ken Hultgren

Majesty
of the Maker

EVIDENCE for DESIGN

A faith-and-science
study guide for individuals
and small groups

Contents

© 2007 Reasons To Believe · P.O. Box 5978, Pasadena, CA 91117
(800) 482-7836 · www.reasons.org

Introduction

The *Majesty of the Maker* series is designed to encourage individuals, small groups, Sunday school classes, and other study groups to further explore the wonders of God's creation and experience the amazing ways He cares for and communicates with us. Each of the five lessons will challenge participants to further investigate the Scriptures and their personal faith with help from credible scholars.

- In lesson 1, RTB's founder and president, Dr. Hugh Ross, shares the role science played in his own spiritual journey. His story exemplifies the scriptural principle of putting everything to the test—the foundation of the scientific method! We will also discuss our own spiritual journey and how science might impact our walk with Christ.

- The second lesson shows how God has revealed Himself to us in two ways—through both the words of the Bible and the facts of nature. Bible scholar Kenneth Samples sheds light on "Two-Books" theology and shows how this idea has been the predominant view of historic Christianity.

- Lesson 3 emphasizes the remarkable scientific accuracy of the Scriptures. Dr. Ross discusses the order of creation established in the first chapter of Genesis and how it matches the latest scientific research.

- JPL research scientist Dr. David Rogstad helps us, in lesson 4, understand just how finely-tuned our planet must be to support life. This session highlights one of the primary messages of Scripture—God's desire for an intimate relationship with humans, His ultimate creation.

- The concluding lesson brings each participant to a better appreciation of God's main purposes in this creation and in the new creation to come. Dr. Ross reveals how God gives each Christian purpose for today and hope for the future.

Beginning each lesson with prayer will help open up discussion and make these topics—new to many people—both more intriguing and more accessible. Reading the Scripture passages and discussing them before viewing the presentations on DVD will allow people to consider the verses prior to being influenced by the featured speaker. Each lesson takes approximately 60 minutes (including DVD viewing and discussion questions). More or less time may be used in each section, depending on the format of your group.

Another option for groups (especially those short on time) is to have each participant complete the first two portions of the study—*What's This all About?* and *Exploring Scripture*—on their own prior to meeting. Then the group can gather, view, and discuss the video portion of the lesson.

The extra sections—*Did You Know?* as well as *Digging Deeper* and *Further Resources*—are included for individual reflection but may also be used during the study time, if desired. Some leaders may choose to assign them as "homework" following the week's discussion.

No scientific background is required, just a willingness to search for answers. If you have any topic-related questions, Reasons To Believe offers an Apologetics Hotline at (626) 335-5282. Trained apologists are available to help 7 days a week from 5:00–7:00 P.M. Pacific Time.

The Leader's Edition of this study is identical to the Participant's Edition except for the inclusion of the DVD. Additional or replacement DVDs are available for purchase by calling Reasons To Believe at (800) 482-7836.

May the majesty of your Maker draw you close and strengthen your faith through this study.

Acknowledgments

Many people have contributed to the publication of this study. Thanks to Willow Creek Community Church and the Church Communication Network (CCN) for partnering with Reasons To Believe and permitting use of the video footage.

Also thanks to the RTB staff who were willing to add this project to their already busy schedules. Personal appreciation goes to Sandra Dimas, Patti Covert, Kathy Ross, Robert and Krista Bontrager, Jonathan Price, Craig Kletzien, Phil Chien, and Esther Attebery.

And lastly, thanks to our RTB volunteer apologists and chapters for their help with the content. People from all over the world have contributed their insights. Special thanks to Bob and Kathy Clapper, Peter Lambros, James Reeverts, and Bob Perry.

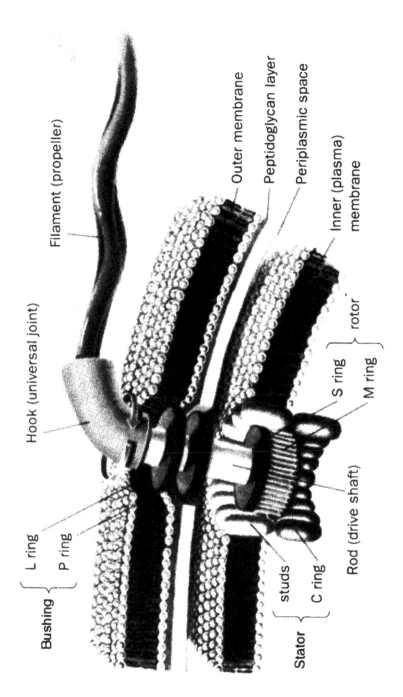

Filament (propeller)

Hook (universal joint)

Outer membrane

Peptidoglycan layer

Periplasmic space

Inner (plasma) membrane

L ring

P ring

Bushing

rotor

S ring

M ring

studs

C ring

Stator

Rod (drive shaft)

THE BIOCHEMICAL COMPLEXITY OF A BACTERIAL FLAGELLUM

Lesson 1
Cosmic Fingerprints

What we have found is evidence for the birth of the universe . . .
If you're religious, it's like looking at God.

—**George Smoot**, atheist astronomer, from interviews
on the COBE discoveries

The heavens declare the glory of God;
the skies proclaim the work of his hands.
—**Psalm 19:1**

What's This all About?
(5 minutes)

"You got your chocolate in my peanut butter!"

"Well, you got your peanut butter on my chocolate!"

This successful advertising campaign illustrates an important point: sometimes seemingly dissimilar things actually go well together—and even complement one another.

What other kinds of things go well together?

Did you mention salt and pepper or a dog and a bone? Did the idea of science and the Bible come up? Some people don't think science and the Bible connect at all. In fact, many people believe they are completely contrary to each other and that the authors of the Bible were ignorant of nature's facts. Christians are often accused of telling people to "just believe" the Bible, to take it on faith—which usually means believing blindly, without any evidence.

Contrary to skeptics' beliefs, the Bible is actually true in all matters it discusses, including matters of science. Scripture even provided the foundation for the scientific method. In this study, we'll look through various biblical passages and see what they say about science and God's creation. We'll hear from Dr. Hugh Ross about how he came to faith in Christ because of his research using the scientific method.

In 1 Thessalonians 5:21, the Bible challenges us to put truth to the test. This idea of testing is the backbone of faith. When the word "faith" (Greek: "*pistis*") is used in Scripture, it does not refer to wishful thinking or blind belief but rather to a strong conviction based on facts. Faith comes from convincing evidence.

Exploring Scripture

(15 minutes)

Read 1 Thessalonians 5:12-23
- How does the invitation to "test everything" contribute to the distinctive nature of the Christian faith?

- In what ways might this invitation appeal to the scientific mind? To the non-scientific mind?

Based on these passages, what are some things that should be put to the test?
- Deuteronomy 13:1-2 and 18:20-22

- Matthew 7:15-23

- Galatians 1:8-9

Read Isaiah 40:25-31
- Why does Isaiah emphasize the importance of acknowledging God as the Creator?

■ Verse 26 says that God knows each of the stars by name. Why should this encourage us? (Hint: Most scientists claim there are approximately 50+ billion trillion stars. That's 5 x 10^{22} or 50,000,000,000,000,000,000,000. By the way—there are only 6.5 billion people on the Earth today. That's 6.5 x 109 or 6,500,000,000.)

Play DVD Lesson 1—Cosmic Fingerprints

(23 minutes)

Hugh Ross *talks about his journey to faith and how his scientific investigation brought him face-to-face with the accuracy and authority of the Bible. Listen to him discuss the scientific method and how its basic principles are found in the Scriptures.*

Questions for Thought

(17 minutes)

1. Why is it important to establish a "frame of reference" when trying to understand either science or the Bible?

2. Many people raise questions about "other religions" when discussing faith-science issues. What part of Dr. Ross's testimony can help you form a strategy to address this problem?

3. Isaiah talks about several key characteristics of the big bang model that would not have been known by scientists at the time of his writing. Can you recall the ones Dr. Ross mentions?

4. Dr. Ross says the Bible has a moral message, a "beautiful standard." What does he say about our ability to live up to that standard?

5. What are some ways in which God shows His majesty and glory through this created world?

6. Dr. Ross states, "When you commit yourself to God's purpose, He paves the way and opens the door for you to fulfill His will in your life." How have you experienced God's work in ways that fulfill His will for you?

Did You Know?

1. The Wilkinson Microwave Anisotropy Probe (WMAP) can look back at the universe when it was only 380,000 years old (pictured below). Comparing the universe (13.7 billion years old) with a 60-year-old person, it would be like seeing a picture of that person as a tiny baby about 14 hours old!

© NASA/WMAP Science Team

2. In 1995, there were 41 design parameters known to be necessary for life to exist on Earth. The probability of all these coming together *without* supernatural intervention was 1 chance in 10^{31}. By 2004, the number of life-essential parameters had increased to 322. The probability of all 322 occurring naturally is 1 chance in 10^{282}. And that number continues to increase! (See www.designevidences.org.)

Digging Deeper

"What Is the Scientific Method?"
Excerpted from *Creation as Science* by Hugh Ross, 42-44

The scientific method, as drawn from the pages of Scripture, addresses the human tendency to form conclusions too quickly and too firmly. This systematic process guards against making any interpretation or hypothesis until certain basic steps are completed. Even after these steps are taken and a hypothesis is formed, it encourages investigators to hold loosely to their initial interpretations.

Consistent application of this step-by-step method encourages the meticulousness, restraint, and humility a truth-quest warrants. Use of the process rests on and even builds on confidence that the natural realm is a well-ordered, consistent, contradiction-free system. This method and this underlying conviction, more than anything else, launched and propelled the scientific revolution of the past four centuries.

The number and wording of steps outlining the scientific method may vary slightly depending on the type of investigation to which it is applied. But its basic components—as used for explaining the origins and history of the universe, life, and humanity—include these tasks in sequential order:

1. Identify the phenomenon to be investigated and explained.

2. Identify the frame(s) of reference or point(s) of view to be used in studying and describing the phenomenon.

3. Determine the initial conditions of the phenomenon.

4. Perform an experiment or observe the phenomenon, noting what takes place when, where, and in what order.

5. Note the final conditions of the phenomenon.

6. Form a tentative explanation, or hypothesis, for how and why things transpired as they did.

7. Test the hypothesis with further experiments or observations.

8. Revise the hypothesis accordingly.

9. Determine how well the explanation of the phenomenon integrates with explanations of related phenomena.

Note: These steps apply just as usefully to biblical interpretation as they do to interpretation of natural events.

While this method does not guarantee objectivity and accuracy, it does minimize the effects of oversight, personal bias, and presuppositions. Even the most careful interpreter possesses only limited knowledge, understanding, and objectivity. Interpretations, no matter how well developed and thoroughly tested, fall short of perfection. Thus, the need for ongoing adjustments and refinements never ends. (Astronomers have measured and observed most of the solar system, but new details—even new objects the size of Pluto—continue to emerge.)

This investigative method works best when practiced continuously and cyclically. It moves researchers closer to the truth, or to a more complete grasp of it, each time they cycle through the steps with new information and insight. Changes will be necessary. New questions and challenges always arise. But that's how knowledge and understanding advance. The process never ends. It's exhilarating for anyone who loves truth.

One of the strengths of this method lies in its built-in quality controls. Appropriate application eliminates bad science. Faulty or grossly incomplete interpretations will be exposed by their need for major corrections. Good interpretations yield progressively smaller revisions with each cycle through the steps. The explanatory power and predictive success of a good hypothesis continue to increase until it becomes a theory. With greater substantiation, the theory expands into a detailed and comprehensive model. Ongoing application of the scientific method continually refines, improves, and extends that model.

The scientific method makes possible a constructive, equitable dialogue about creation and evolution. All who wish to participate may present their models—interpretive scenarios developed and refined by observations and testing—for comparison. The models that demonstrate the greatest explanatory power and predictive success remain on the table for further study. Those requiring larger and larger revisions after failing predictive tests can be eliminated. The field narrows, through time, focusing on the model (or set of models) that most closely corresponds with reality. And, as the more successful models mature, they multiply into more detailed variants.

No doubt this process often involves emotion. Researchers, like other people, can become attached to their ideas, but when they bring their attachments and personal biases into the open, rather than concealing them, science can advance more freely and productively.

Within the realm of scientific research, a model's failure carries no great stigma. So-called failed models often illuminate and foster the growth of successful models. Determining what does not work often helps elucidate what does.

When all participants remain committed to follow the findings wherever they lead, they can work in partnership through failures, successes, and disagreements. They can resolve disputes and solve mysteries. Recent progress in cosmology toward a more precise and comprehensive model for cosmic origins and developments provides an illuminating example. This progress shows that truth can and does ultimately prevail on creation/evolution questions despite ideological, philosophical, and theological preferences and commitments.

Further Resources

Jastrow, Robert. *God and the Astronomers*. 2nd ed. New York: Norton, 2000.

Journey Toward Creation. 2nd ed. Multilingual 70 min. Reasons To Believe in association with Global Net Productions. DVD. 2003.

Newman, Robert C., and Herman J. Eckelmann Jr. *Genesis One and the Origin of the Earth*. 1977. Reprint. Hatfield, PA: Interdisciplinary Biblical Research Institute, 2000.

Ross, Hugh. *The Creator and the Cosmos: How the Greatest Scientific Discoveries of the Century Reveal God*. 3rd ed. Colorado Springs, CO: NavPress, 2001.

Ross, Hugh. *The Genesis Question: Scientific Advances and the Accuracy of Genesis*. 2nd. ed. Colorado Springs, CO: NavPress, 2001.

Lesson 2
Dual Revelation

For since the creation of the world God's invisible qualities—
his eternal power and divine nature—have been clearly seen, being under-
stood from what has been made, so that men are without excuse.

—**Romans 1:20**

What's This all About?

(5 minutes)

Memories of places we've been and things we've seen fill our lives. Can you think of a place you've visited that has inspired or impacted you? What was so impressive about what you experienced? How did you feel?

Most likely, this memory centered around something created—either by human or divine hands. It could be the Great Wall of China, Yosemite's Half Dome, St. Paul's Cathedral, the Grand Canyon, or a beautiful sunset.

The magnificence of these places inspires wonder and awe within us. When we think about God's creation and the magnificence we see through telescopes and microscopes as well as the naked eye, we stand in amazement of God's power and love. Scripture speaks many times about this splendor. In fact, the Bible tells us God's creation is one way He reveals His glory. Psalm 19:1 says, "The heavens declare the glory of God; the skies proclaim the work of his hands."

Most Christians already know that God has revealed Himself in the words of the Bible. But in this lesson, we will investigate how God has also revealed Himself through His creation. Not only do we stand in awe of His creative power, but we understand His character more clearly by what we see in the world around us.

Exploring Scripture

(15 minutes)

Read Psalm 19:1-11

▮ What are some ways, according to this Psalm, we can know God?

▮ List some characteristics of God that are revealed through
    ▮ Nature (His world)

    ▮ Scripture (His Word)

▮ Can you describe some truths about God revealed through nature
that correlate clearly with what you read of God in Scripture?

Read Romans 1:16-21

■ How has God shown Himself to people, and what can we know about Him through this revelation?

Read John 14:9-11, Colossians 1:15-20, and Hebrews 1:1-3.

■ In what ways is Jesus the ultimate revelation of God?

Play DVD Lesson 2 — Dual Revelation

(25 minutes)

Kenneth Samples shares how God has made Himself known through both the words of the Bible and the world of creation. Samples introduces us to the Two-Books doctrine stated more than 400 years ago in the Belgic Confession.

Questions for Thought

(15 minutes)

1. Now that you have been introduced to the concept of nature as God's "other book" of revelation to us, how might this awareness be used to better share the message of the Gospel?

2. If these two forms of revelation seem at odds with one another, what would be your approach to resolving the conflict?

3. What passages in the Bible can be corroborated or clarified through a better understanding of general revelation (that is, nature)?

4. What does Kenneth Samples mean by the term "cosmic cathedral"?

5. Have you ever experienced a revival of your soul through Scripture? Give an example.

Did You Know?

1. The official teaching of the Roman Catholic Church in the early seventeenth century was that passages like Psalm 93:1—which describe the Earth being fixed, established, or unmoving—should be taken concretely. But a growing body of physical evidence showed this interpretation was not accurate. Galileo (a scientist and Christian) offered the first observational proof that the Earth is not, in fact, fixed, but rotates on its axis and revolves around the Sun along with other planets. Today, mainstream Christians don't think this issue is controversial at all. It's generally understood that the Bible was misinterpreted and that further discoveries in the record of nature corrected this misunderstanding.

2. The Belgic Confession is actually the personal profession of faith of one person, Guido de Brès. It was written in the early days of the Reformation in what was then the southern part of the Netherlands (known today as Belgium). The Spanish King Philip II viewed himself as the divinely-ordained protector of Roman Catholicism. He wanted to defeat Protestantism, especially in the Netherlands, where growing prosperity and an independent spirit seemed to threaten Spain and the monarchy. Reformed congregations met secretly in many major cities and towns. In May 1566 they gathered in a secret synod at Antwerp, seeking a common confession. They adopted the confession of Guido de Brès with some revisions and sent it to Geneva for printing. Today, the Belgic Confession is widely used as a summary of the Christian faith. Article 2 explains God's dual revelation.

Belgic Confession
Article 2: The Means by Which We Know God

We know him by two means:

First, by the creation, preservation, and government of the universe, since that universe is before our eyes like a beautiful book in which all creatures, great and small, are as letters to make us ponder the invisible things of God: his eternal power and his divinity, as the apostle Paul says in Romans 1:20.

All these things are enough to convict men and to leave them without excuse.

Second, he makes himself known to us more openly by his holy and divine Word, as much as we need in this life, for his glory and for the salvation of his own.

Digging Deeper

Adapted from "The Historic Alliance of Christianity and Science"
Available at http://www.reasons.org/resources/faf/98q3faf/98q3apol.shtml.
by Kenneth Richard Samples

Many people view Christianity as unscientific at best and anti-scientific at worst.

Conflicts between scientific theories and the Christian faith have arisen throughout the centuries, but the level of conflict has often been exaggerated. And Christianity's positive influence on scientific progress is seldom acknowledged.[1]

The intellectual climate that gave rise to modern science (roughly three centuries ago) was decisively shaped by Christianity.[2] Not only were most of the earliest scientists themselves devout Christians (including Copernicus, Kepler, Galileo, Newton, Boyle, and Pascal),[3] but the Christian worldview also provided a basis for science to emerge and flourish. Christian theism affirmed that an infinite, eternal, and personal God created the world *ex nihilo*. The creation, reflecting the rational nature of the Creator, was therefore orderly and uniform. Further, humankind was uniquely created in God's image (Gen. 1:26-27) and thus capable of reasoning and discovering the intelligibility of the created order. In effect, the Christian worldview supported the underlying principles that made scientific inquiry possible and desirable.

Eminent historian and philosopher of science Stanley Jaki has argued that science was "stillborn" in other great civilizations outside Europe because prevailing ideas such as a cyclical approach to time, an astrological approach to the heavens, and metaphysical views that either deified nature (animism) or denied it (idealism) stifled scientific development.[4]

Even the principles underlying the scientific method (testability, verification/falsification) arise from the Judeo-Christian Scriptures.[5] Because the founders of modern science believed that the heavens genuinely declare the glory of God (Ps. 19:1), they possessed both the necessary conceptual framework and the spiritual incentive to boldly explore nature's mysteries. According to Christian theism, God has disclosed Himself in two dynamic ways: through special revelation (God's redemptive actions recorded in the Bible—His book) and general revelation (God's creative actions discoverable in nature—His world). Puritan scientists in England and America viewed the study of science as a sacred attempt to "think God's thoughts after Him."[6]

Christians have plenty of room to grow in the virtues of discernment, reflection, and vigorous analysis, and the wisdom literature of the Old Testament consistently exhorts God's people to exercise them. The New Testament teaches this same message (see Col. 2:8; 1 Thes. 5:21; 1 Jn. 4:1). These principles provided the backdrop for the emerging experimental method.

The existence of an objectively real world, the comprehensibility of that world, the reliability of sense perception and human rationality, the orderliness and uniformity of nature, and the validity of mathematics and logic are some of the philosophical presuppositions foundational to the study of science.[7] These necessary preconditions are rooted in Christian theism's claims of an infinite, eternal, and personal Creator who carefully ordered the universe and provided man with a mind that corresponds to the universe's intelligibility. This theistic schema served as the intellectual breeding ground for modern science, sustaining and enabling it to flourish.

How does naturalism compare? Does it explain or provide fertile ground for the birth and progress of science?

Consider the way a naturalist might answer the following questions: How can a world that is the product of blind, non-purposeful processes account for and justify the crucial conditions that make the scientific enterprise possible? How does naturalism justify the inductive method, assumptions about the uniformity of nature, and the existence of abstract non-empirical entities such as numbers, propositions, and the laws of logic if the world is the product of a mindless accident? According to naturalism, isn't the human mind just one accident in a series of many accidents?[8] If so, how can anyone have confidence that it steers a person toward truth? How could such a concept as truth even be conceived?

The prevailing scientific notions of big bang cosmology and the emerging anthropic principle are uniquely compatible with Christian theism. Because the universe had a singular beginning, it's logical to inquire about its cause. Gottfried Leibniz's classic question, "Why is there something rather than nothing?" seems even more provocative in light of what is now known about the universe. Is it more reasonable to believe that everything came into existence from nothing by nothing or that "in the beginning God created the heavens and the earth"?[9]

References

1. See Charles E. Hummel, *The Galileo Connection: Resolving Conflicts Between Science and the Bible* (Downers Grove, IL: InterVarsity Press, 1986).

2. See Stanley Jaki, *Science and Creation: From Eternal Cycles to an Oscillating Universe* (Scottish Academic Press, 1974); R. Hooykaas, *Religion and the Rise of Modern Science* (Grand Rapids, MI: Eerdmans, 1972); and Eric V. Snow, "Christianity: A Cause of Modern Science?" http://rae.org/jaki.html (accessed August 4, 1998).

3. See Hummel, *Galileo Connection*. While Newton was a serious student of the Bible, serious questions have been raised about whether his theological views were thoroughly orthodox.

4. Jaki, *Science and Creation*.

5. Kenneth L. Woodward, "How the Heavens Go," *Newsweek*, July 20, 1998, 52.

6. See Hummel, *Galileo Connection*, 162.

7. See Hummel, 158-159. For a more detailed discussion of the philosophical presuppositions of science, see J. P. Moreland, ed., *The Creation Hypothesis: Scientific Evidence for an Intelligent Designer* (Downers Grove, IL: InterVarsity Press, 1994), 17.

8. Richard Taylor, *Metaphysics*, 4th ed. (Englewood Cliffs, NJ: Prentice Hall, 1992), 110-112.

9. Genesis 1:1 (NIV).

Further Resources

Collins, C. John. *Science & Faith: Friends or Foes?* Wheaton, IL: Crossway Books, 2003.

Erickson, Millard J. *Christian Theology*. 2nd ed. Grand Rapids. MI: Baker, 1998.

Geisler, Norman L., and Paul K. Hoffman, eds. *Why I Am a Christian: Leading Thinkers Explain Why They Believe*. Grand Rapids, MI: Baker, 2001.

God's Two-Part Harmony: Scripture and Nature. CD. 200 min. Reasons To Believe, 2003.

Morris, Leon. *I Believe in Revelation*. London: Hodder & Stoughton, 1976.

Samples, Kenneth Richard. *Without A Doubt: Answering the 20 Toughest Faith Questions*. Grand Rapids, MI: Baker, 2004.

Warfield, Benjamin B. *The Inspiration and Authority of the Bible*. Ed. Samuel G. Craig. London: Marshall, Morgan & Scott, 1951.

Lesson 3
Genesis Miracles

So long as the universe had a beginning, we could suppose it had a creator.
But if the universe is really completely self-contained, having no boundary
or edge, it would have neither beginning nor end: it would simply be.
What place, then, for a creator?

—**Stephen Hawking**, *A Brief History of Time*

What's This all About?
(5 minutes)

Why do you think so many people hold the Genesis account of creation as a fantasy or myth? Have you ever struggled with reconciling what Genesis 1 says with what scientists are saying?

The amazing thing about Scripture is that it communicates God's truth in a way all generations and all peoples can understand. Nature continuously confirms the Bible's scientific accuracy even though its words were written thousands of years before the development of modern science. A great example of this consistency is the big bang theory. In the past 100 years or so, scientists have discovered that the universe (matter, energy, time, and space) had a beginning and is still expanding from an infinitesimally small starting point. As the comment by Stephen Hawking suggests, a beginning implies a creator.

Another recent discovery focuses on the Cambrian explosion. It can be considered the "big bang" of life. Over half the animal phyla on Earth today came into existence in a geological instant about 543 million years ago. The evolutionary paradigm does not have a logical or consistent explanation for this breathtaking event. On the other hand, a biblical creation model predicts the sudden appearance of various life-forms throughout the fossil record. (Please see *Creation as Science* for a detailed explanation of Reasons To Believe's testable creation model.)

Genesis 1 makes thirteen statements (or "predictions" in scientific terms) regarding the order of the creation events. Amazingly, Moses got them right. He placed all thirteen events in the proper order. No other holy book even comes close!

In this lesson we'll look through several major creation passages in Scripture with astronomer Hugh Ross and explore a detailed explanation of the Genesis miracles. Their accuracy will encourage your faith, and perhaps the compelling case for the inspiration of the Bible will motivate you to share this information with others.

Exploring Scripture
(20 minutes)

Read Genesis 1:20-27
▪ What does the creation account in these verses tell us about the unique place of human beings in the created order?

Read Psalm 104
▪ What scientific content can you find within this chapter? Do you see any parallels with the "days" described in Genesis 1?

Read Hebrews 4:1-11

- Discuss the various meanings of the word "rest." Do these verses suggest that God is still in His seventh day of rest? If so, what do they say about humans entering this rest?

Play DVD Lesson 3 — Genesis Miracles

(16 minutes)

Hugh Ross gives an overview of the first chapter of Genesis focusing on the order of creation miracles and how they align with the scientific facts. Dr. Ross also discusses the importance of integrating other creation passages.

Questions for Thought

(20 minutes)

1. Dr. Ross refers to thirteen creation events highlighted in the opening chapter of Genesis. How many of these can you identify using your Bible.

2. Why is it important to understand the frame(s) of reference when interpreting Genesis 1?

3. What are the implications of recognizing that the phrase "the heavens and the earth" refers to the entire universe and all its components?

4. Some critics say that the Genesis creation account is silly and contradictory because it claims light was created on Day One while stars and planets were created on Day Four. How would you answer these critics by integrating verses 1-3 with the events of Day Four?

5. Why is it important that the Bible gives us many different creation accounts?

6. What is the significance that in Genesis 1 each of the first six days is bracketed by "evening and morning" while the seventh day is not? (See Hebrews 4 for clarification.)

7. How does the fact that the order of miracles presented in Genesis is scientifically accurate inspire your faith and help you share the Gospel with others?

Did You Know?

1. As Dr. Ross mentions, the statistical odds against an ancient author's placing all thirteen acts of creation mentioned in Genesis 1 in the scientifically correct order are staggering: 1 chance in 6,227,020,800!

2. The early Earth rotated at the rate of one complete spin every 6-7 hours. At that rate, only small bacteria could survive; surface wind speeds reached several hundred miles per hour! About 50 million years after the formation of the Earth, a collision with a Mars-sized object sent tons of debris into orbit. This debris coalesced to form the Moon. The effects of its gravity eventually slowed Earth's rotation to a safe and relatively consistent 24 hours so advanced life could exist.

3. Here are 25 creation accounts in Scripture which deal with issues related to creation and the natural world:

- Genesis 1
- Genesis 2
- Genesis 3-5
- Genesis 6-9
- Genesis 10-11
- Job 9
- Job 34-42
- Psalm 8
- Psalm 19

- Psalm 33
- Psalm 65
- Psalm 104
- Psalm 139
- Psalms 147-148
- Proverbs 8
- Ecclesiastes 1-3
- Ecclesiastes 8-12
- Isaiah 40-51

- Romans 1-8
- 1 Corinthians 15
- 2 Corinthians 4
- Hebrews 1
- Hebrews 4
- 2 Peter 3
- Revelation 20-22

Digging Deeper

Rest: Day Seven

Excerpted from *The Genesis Question* by Hugh Ross, 63-65

With the creation of the human species—male and female—Earth's only spirit beings designed "in the image of God," the activity of God's creative week ends. Genesis 1 reaches its jubilant climax. But the week isn't over yet. There's one more day.

"By the seventh day God had finished the work he had been doing; so on the seventh day he rested from all his work. And God blessed the seventh day and made it holy, because on it he rested from all the work of creating he had done" (Genesis 2:2-3).

Does the word "rest" imply that God grew weary? A look into the Hebrew text sheds light, but even a moment's reflection on the English translation can help. The Hebrew word for "rested" is *shabat*. It carries a meaning mentioned in some biblical footnotes as "ceased." Anyone who has studied music will recognize that this meaning also applies to the English word "rest." When musicians come to a certain symbol in their musical score, they *rest*, or cease, from sounding their instrument for as long as the symbol indicates. Their cessation has nothing to do with weariness (though they may be glad for a breather).

God blessed that day and made it holy, setting it apart as a day to rest, or cease, from His work of creating. He also set up a rest day (twenty-four hours) for humans and a rest "day" (one year) for tilled land, knowing what would be best for each.

The Seventh Day Continues

Each of the six creation days closes with the same refrain: "There was evening, and there was morning," then the day's number. The statement suggests that each day had a start time (to begin with evening makes sense since the creation days began in darkness and ended in light) and an end time. However, the refrain is not attached to the seventh day. Its closure is missing.

Given the consistency of this element in the account of the first six days, its absence from the account of the seventh day can be taken as a meaningful hint: the day has not ended. The interpretation receives confirmation in other portions of Scripture. Psalm 95:7-11, John 5:16-18, and Hebrews 4:1-11, each passage the work of a different writer, declaring that the seventh creation day began after the creation of Adam and Eve, continues through the present, and extends into the future. Revelation 21 reveals that the seventh day will eventually come to an end (after evil is conquered) as God resumes His creative endeavors in the making of a new heaven and earth, a new cosmos with new physical laws, appropriate, as always, to the fulfillment of His divine purposes and plans.

The scientific record, as well as Scripture, affirms the continuance of the seventh day, the cessation of divine creative activity. According to the fossil record, new life-forms proliferated through the millions of years before modern humans arrived on the scene. Though frequent extinctions occurred through many millennia, the introduction rate for new species matched or outstripped the extinction rate. Then came the humans.

In the years of human history, the extinction rate has increased significantly—some environmentalists would say frighteningly—because of human activity. Removing the human factor still leaves an extinction rate of at least one species per year. The introduction rate, however, suddenly plummeted to a virtual zero. According to biologists Paul and Anne Ehrlich, "The production of a new animal species in nature has yet to be documented."

Botanists argue for ongoing speciation. Field observers have documented some distinguishable differentiation. Whether all of these new plants deserve distinct "species" labels remains a debatable question. Many scientists see most of the new plants merely as new breeds, or strains, of the old, rather than as new species. Whatever the case, no one denies the glaring imbalance of extinction and speciation.

Physical conditions on Earth before Adam and Eve, during the era of species proliferation, compared to now, have not changed dramatically. Research indicates that the natural evolutionary process, the observable "microevolution," occurs at roughly the same rate today as it did before humans. Science offers no explanation, as yet, for the sudden change in the speciation rate, but the Bible offers one: the difference comes from the change in God's level of creative activity. Before Adam and Eve, it was high. After Adam and Eve, it dropped to zero (with respect to physical life).

Further Resources

Godfrey, W. Robert. *God's Pattern for Creation: A Covenantal Reading of Genesis 1*. Phillipsburg, NJ: P & R Publishing, 2003.

Ross, Hugh. *Creation as Science: A Testable Model Approach to End the Creation/ Evolution Wars*. Colorado Springs, CO: NavPress, 2006.

Ross, Hugh. *Genesis One: A Scientific Perspective*. 4th ed. Glendora, CA: Reasons To Believe, 2006.

Ross, Hugh. *The Genesis Question: Scientific Advances and the Accuracy of Genesis*. 2nd ed. Colorado Springs, CO: NavPress, 2001.

Ross, Hugh. *A Matter of Days: Resolving a Creation Controversy*. Colorado Springs, CO: NavPress, 2004.

Stoner, Don. *A New Look at an Old Earth: Resolving the Conflict Between the Bible and Science*. Eugene, OR: Harvest House, 1997.

Lesson 4
Earth: A Great Place to Live

A review of habitable zones—for animals as well as microbes,
and in the galaxy and Universe as well as around our sun—
leads to an inescapable conclusion: Earth is a rare place indeed.

—From *Rare Earth,* by **Peter D. Ward** (paleontologist)
& **Donald Brownlee** (astrobiologist)

What's This all About?

(5 minutes)

Extraterrestrial life has been a hot topic for years. Just look at the success of movies and TV shows such as *Star Wars, ET, Star Trek,* and, of course, *Galaxy Quest*! Each of these programs features alien civilizations. Such shows are pure science fiction, but their popularity may reflect the inclination of many people to believe there are hundreds of planets capable of supporting life elsewhere in the universe.

In one of the scenes from the movie Contact (based on the writings of popular scientist Carl Sagan), Jodie Foster's character, astronomer Ellie Arroway, says, *"there are 400 billion stars out there, just in our galaxy alone. If only one out of a million of those had planets, and if just one out of a million of those had life, and if just one of a million of those had intelligent life, there would be literally millions of civilizations out here."*

What is your response to this statement? How abundant do you think life may be in our universe? What are the chances that researchers will be able to find a planet out there that can support life?

A look at the latest scientific research shows that the possibility of finding another life-supporting planet like Earth is shrinking dramatically, even though the technical capabilities for searching deeper into space continue to increase. The reason: Our planet has so many finely tuned characteristics that the probability of another life-supporting planet is statistically approaching zero.

In the 1970s, Carl Sagan estimated that about 10 percent of planets throughout the universe had the required conditions for life. Scientists now know this estimation is incorrect. Of the more than 200 planets detected to date, not one is even close to being able to support life.

In this lesson, we will look at how unique our planet really is and how perfectly it's located in the entire expanse of the universe. Scripture tells us that God has fine-tuned everything to provide us with a home, but as Dr. David Rogstad explains, science reveals that Earth is really the *only* place to be!

Exploring Scripture

(15 minutes)

Read Genesis 2:8-14
▪ How does this passage convey that God carefully created a special place for human beings to live?

Read Psalm 8, 19:1
▪ According to the psalmist, what is the purpose of creation?

- Although humans might appear insignificant compared to the expanse of the universe, they have been exalted by God. What do these verses suggest about the place God has prepared for us to live?

Play DVD Lesson 4—Earth: A Great Place to Live
(20 minutes)

David Rogstad earned a Ph.D. in physics from Caltech before launching his career as a rocket scientist. He also led the technical team credited with saving the Galileo Mission to Jupiter. During his research, he has continually been impressed with the uniqueness of Earth's location. Dr. Rogstad's insight provides more reasons to be grateful for how the Lord has hand-placed humanity's home for our benefit.

Questions for Thought
(20 minutes)

1. What is meant in the scientific literature by the term "habitable zone"? Describe some of the specific properties of a habitable zone (Dr. Rogstad mentions five).

2. What are some examples of uninhabitable places in the universe?

3. Earth's solar system resides in a spiral galaxy. Explain the structure of this galaxy and describe some of the characteristics that allow it to support life on Earth.

4. How does the information in this lesson influence your thinking with regard to "extraterrestrial life"?

5. What factors in Dr. Rogstad's arguments seem most convincing? How can you use these to encourage other believers?

Did You Know?

1. Scientists may well discover remains of microbial life on the planet Mars! However, this possibility does not mean life originated there. It is estimated that up to several million tons of Earth debris have traveled to and settled on Mars over the 4-billion-plus years of Earth's history.

2. The moon is so large in comparison to Earth that the pair has sometimes been called a double-planet system.

3. Earth's location in the Milky Way Galaxy is unique not just for its ability to support life, but also for giving us the capability to recognize its rarity. This feature is considered the "measurability" of our location. We reside in a place far enough away from the center of Earth's galaxy that light does not dominate the sky. So, we can look through telescopes to observe and study how the universe came to be the way it is today. Earth's unique location has allowed us to discover the nature of the universe, the enormity of its size, the complexity of its arrangement, and the degree of its fine-tuning to support life. It is eerily fascinating that the very factors that permit us to inhabit Earth are the same ones that have allowed us to discover these facts.

Digging Deeper
(20 minutes)

Adapted from "Habitable Planets Rarer than Originally Thought"
Connections, Q4 2006, by Jeffrey Zweerink, 2-3

Twenty years ago, the nine solar system planets (now eight by vote of the International Astronomical Union, which demoted Pluto[1]) were the only known planets in the universe. Lacking the ability to make direct observations, most astronomers assumed that planetary systems would be abundant and that such systems would bear a strong resemblance to ours. But in recent years, the first accurate glimpses of distant systems began pouring in with surprising results.

By August 2006, astronomers had discovered more than 200 extrasolar planets (including 148 stars with single planets and 20 stars with multiple planets). Virtually all are gas giants similar to Jupiter. Their detection enabled scientists to assess the possibility that an Earth-like planet, capable of supporting long-standing liquid water, could exist around these stars.

Contrary to expectations, none of these planetary systems resemble the one in which we live. All of the extrasolar gas giants either have a more-eccentric orbit than Jupiter's or orbit their stars more closely than Jupiter orbits the Sun. Consequently, the gravitational instabilities resulting from the planets' orbits in most of the systems would eject any Earth-like planet into interstellar space. Still, astronomers found that in a few systems, Earth-like planets could be stable for a long time.

Because a hypothetical habitable planet might remain stable in a small fraction of known systems, astronomers narrowed their search by investigating whether an Earth-like planet could even form in such systems. Using Monte Carlo simulations,[2] a University of Colorado astrophysicist studied how the existence of gas giants with specific orbits influences the subsequent formation of any habitable terrestrial planets.[3] The simulations revealed that any gas giant with an orbit slightly smaller than Jupiter's prevented the formation of watery terrestrial planets. Additionally, if the gas-giant's orbit was not exactly circular, it had to be even farther from the star to permit formation of an Earth-like planet. However, this position makes the terrestrial planet less habitable, as increasing the gas-giant's distance from the star diminishes its capacity to shield the terrestrial planet from comet and asteroid impacts.

Even this picture is not complete, however. Astronomers know from the calculated orbits of the gas giants that they must have migrated into their current orbits from the locations where they formed. A group of astrophysicists simulated how this migration would affect the formation of habitable terrestrial planets in four systems where a terrestrial planet appears stable.[4] The simulations showed that the migrations completely disrupted habitable-planet formation in three systems. In the fourth system, planets up to six-tenths the mass of Earth could form if (1) the gas-giant migration occurred very early, (2) the known gas-giant orbit is well determined, and (3) no other gas giants exist in the system. (A terrestrial planet just over half an Earth mass likely cannot support the long-standing plate tectonics critical for advanced life, but no planets larger than 0.63 Earth masses formed in the simulations.) Additionally, the chance of forming any potentially habitable terrestrial planet diminishes dramatically if any of the three conditions are not met, particularly if the migration does not occur rapidly.

Such exquisite fine-tuning provides a sobering reminder of the difficulty of the task. As scientists' understanding of planetary formation increases and their simulations become more realistic, the precision required in the process becomes more apparent. And, the naturalistic expectation of finding habitable terrestrial planets around other stars continues to diminish. In contrast, the latest scientific findings increasingly reveal the fingerprints of a supernatural Creator who intervened in cosmic history to ensure a life-supporting environment: Earth.

References

1. See "The Final IAU Resolution on the Definition of 'Planet' Ready for Voting," http://www.iau2006.org/mirror/www.iau.org/iau0602/index.html (accessed January 16, 2006).

2. For more information on Monte Carlo simulations, see David Rogstad's article, "Beating the Odds in Monte Carlo," *Connections* 8, no. 4 (2006), 8.

3. Sean N. Raymond, "The Search for Other Earths: Limits on the Giant Planet Orbits that Allow Habitable Terrestrial Planets to Form," *Astrophysical Journal Letters* 643 (2006): L131-L134.

4. Sean N. Raymond, Rory Barnes, and Nathan A. Kaib, "Predicting Planets in Known Extrasolar Planetary Systems. III. Forming Terrestrial Planets," *Astrophysical Journal* 644 (2006): 1223-1231.

Further Resources

Ross, Hugh, *The Creator and the Cosmos: How the Latest Scientific Discoveries Reveal God*. 3rd ed. Colorado Springs, CO: NavPress, 2001.

Ross, Hugh, Kenneth Samples, and Mark Clark. *Lights in the Sky and Little Green Men: A Rational Christian Look at UFOs and Extraterrestrials*. (Colorado Springs, CO: NavPress, 2001).

The RUFO Hypothesis. Moderated by Greg Koukl, with Hugh Ross, Kenneth Samples, and Mark Clark. 120 min. Reasons To Believe, 2002. DVD

Taylor, Stuart Ross. *Destiny or Chance: Our Solar System and its Place in the Cosmos*. New York: Cambridge University Press, 2000.

Ward, Peter D., and Donald Brownlee. *Rare Earth: Why Complex Life Is Uncommon in the Universe*. New York: Springer, 2003.

Webb, Stephen. *If the Universe Is Teeming with Aliens . . . Where Is Everybody? Fifty Solutions to the Fermi Paradox and the Problem of Extraterrestrial Life*. New York: Springer, 2002.

Lesson 5
Hope, Purpose, and Destiny

*We take the side of science in spite of the patent absurdity
of some of its constructs . . . because we have a prior commitment,
a commitment to materialism. . . . Moreover, that materialism is absolute,
for we cannot allow a Divine Foot in the door.*

—from a book review by **Richard Lewontin**,
atheist, evolutionary biologist

*Then I saw a new heaven and a new earth, for the first heaven
and the first earth had passed away . . . He will wipe every tear
from their eyes. There will be no more death or mourning or
crying or pain, for the old order of things has passed away.*

—**Revelation 21:1, 4**

What's This all About?

(5 minutes)

"I can't wait for my new body." We've often heard this phrase from
Christians who are struggling with health problems. Just think—no more
suffering, no more pain, no more bad-hair days! Paul says in 1 Corinthians
2:9, "No eye has seen, no ear has heard, no mind has conceived what God
has prepared for those who love him." What kind of images do you have
in mind of what heaven will be like?

Did you know that not just our bodies will change, but all the physics we
experience here on Earth will probably change as well? Somehow, in the
new creation there will be no night and people won't need a lamp or the
light of the Sun to see (Revelation 22:5). It seems there will be no gravity,
or at least not the same kind. The size of the new Jerusalem mentioned in
Revelation 21:16 (a cube about 1,500 miles on each side) is not physically

possible given the laws of gravity we experience today. Anything that size would be forced by gravity into a roughly spherical shape.

In this lesson, we get to look into the future. We'll study some verses that give a glimpse of what the Lord is preparing for us. We'll also hear some scientific evidence from Dr. Hugh Ross that gives us more reason to hope in the new and eternal creation.

Exploring Scripture

(15 minutes)

Read Ecclesiastes 6:3-12

▪ The writer talks about the futility of a life without purpose. Is the writer justified in coming to this conclusion?

▪ To what extent do you think this idea reflects the views of those who don't believe in God?

Read Revelation 21-22

■ Take note of the descriptive statements about what the new creation will be like (features, laws, etc.). How do these characteristics differ from those of our existing universe?

■ In these chapters, what is the most encouraging statement to you?

Play DVD Lesson 5—Hope, Purpose, and Destiny

(22 minutes)

Hugh Ross discusses the Humanist Manifesto and how its conclusions (based on a naturalistic perspective) only lead to a hopeless future. In contrast, the Christian doctrine of a second (new) creation gives wonderful hope to believers that this existing world not only serves a crucial purpose but also that our finite existence leads to eternity in the presence of God.

Questions for Thought

(15 minutes)

1. What are the four affirmations of humanism listed by *Free Inquiry* magazine to which Dr. Ross refers in the video? What do they imply about those who believe in God?

2. What is your first reaction to the humanist affirmations after hearing the conclusions of Lawrence Krauss and Glenn Starkman on the gloomy predicament of humanity?

3. Dr. Ross mentions that humans exist at a perfect time and place. What is the basis for such a statement, and what does it suggest about our expectations of life here?

4. How would you define the anthropic principle? How does this idea strengthen your argument for the Christian faith?

Did You Know?

1. Scientists expect a supernova event to drastically impact the Earth's environment in the next 5,000 to 10,000 years.

2. Historical trends of ice ages indicate that we should have experienced an ice age in the past couple thousand years. Planting corn, raising cows, and burning fossil fuels may have helped delay this environmental change.

3. Roughly every 2.5 million years, the Earth's orbit changes enough to initiate an ice age. Such an event will wipe out major animal species.

4. Due to modern-day affluence and technology, the birthrate in many countries has been drastically reduced. Europe, for example, now has a negative population growth due to lower birthrates. Also, people of affluent areas tend to have children later in life, which in turn increases the incidence of harmful mutations.

Digging Deeper
(20 minutes)

"Why the Universe Is the Way It Is"
Available at http://www.reasons.org/resources/connections/200601_connections_q1/
index.shtml# why_the_universe_is_the_way_it_is
by Hugh Ross

In the best-selling science book of all time, author Stephen Hawking explains that no human is content until he or she has answers to the following questions: "What is the nature of the universe? What is our place in it and where did it and we come from? Why is it the way it is?"[1]

From a naturalistic perspective the pain, death, decay, and evil that humans and all life experience serve no real purpose. They simply are the consequence of a random set of cosmic coincidences that permit life to exist.

In countless publications and lectures, naturalists assert that the Christian explanation for the origin, structure, and history of the universe—a biblical creation model—cannot be correct. Why not? A God as powerful, caring, and knowledgeable as Christians claim should have done a much better job of creating. "Your God has other options," they complain. "He could have built a better universe, one without these bad things in it."

God's Purposes in Creating

The first fallacy I see in this charge lies in its assumption that God's sole purpose in creating the universe would (or should) have been to provide a perfectly comfortable environment for life, and especially human life. A second fallacy lies in the assumption that God intended this creation to be *it*, the one and only permanent home for humanity—that is, paradise.

From a Christian perspective, God could have had innumerable reasons for creating the universe, Earth, and life in the manner He did. The Bible declares one reason (number 1 below) and I see implications of at least six more:

1. to manifest and declare His divine attributes, specifically His glory, power, righteousness, wisdom, involvement, and love

2. to provide a suitable habitat for a variety of physical life and for human beings in particular

3. to provide the physical and historical context for God the Son to take human form and accomplish the reconciliation of man to God

4. to provide the necessary resources for the human race to rapidly develop civilization and technology and to achieve global occupation

5. to provide humanity with the best possible viewing platform for discovering—even measuring—expressions of God's glory, power, wisdom, and love

6. to provide a theatre for the rapid (in astronomical terms), efficient conquest of evil

7. to provide human beings with the preparation and training they will need to fulfill their purposes and fully enjoy their reward in the new creation

While these themes offer some insight into God's reasons for creating as He did—especially that Christ would accomplish redemption—a *complete* biblical creation model is unattainable, and no one should be surprised that a few puzzling features remain incompletely explained.

The key point, however, is that everyone should stand utterly amazed that God could create a single universe that can accomplish so much—and with such effectiveness and efficiency. The skeptics who claim they could do better would do well to ponder what it takes to design a universe that can simultaneously fulfill even a few of the purposes mentioned. I sometimes challenge them to try.

Second Creation

A critical distinctive of the biblical creation accounts compared to other creation scenarios is the promise of a new creation that will someday replace the present creation. This new creation goes beyond "paradise restored." It is a radically and gloriously different creation, governed by different laws and framed by different dimensions.[2]

According to Romans and Revelation, the universe in which we presently reside awaits deliverance from its current limitations, including the presence of sin and its consequences.[3] When God's plan—through Christ—to redeem the full number of fallen humans has been accomplished, this universe will have fulfilled its purposes. At that time, God will remove this universe from existence and introduce us to a far superior creation. To put it another way, the present creation is the perfect creation for God to accomplish His redemptive plan and to conquer evil in the process. The new creation that will follow is the perfect creation in which God can lavish

His love upon those humans who have accepted, by His grace, the offer of redemption from sin.

The promise of a new creation to replace the present creation implies that God has purposes for humanity beyond those listed above. Thus, while human beings are equipped to value and enjoy the present creation, in the new creation they will need new and far greater capacities for love and delight.[4] In 1 Corinthians 2:9 the apostle Paul reminds us that "as it is written, no eye has seen, no ear has heard, no mind has conceived what God has prepared for those who love him."

References

1. Stephen Hawking, *A Brief History of Time*, updated and expanded ed. (New York: Bantam, 1996), 187.

2. Hugh Ross, *Beyond the Cosmos: The Extra-Dimensionality of God; What Recent Discoveries in Astrophysics Reveal about the Glory and Love of God*, 2nd ed. (Colorado Springs, CO: NavPress, 1999), 217-228.

3. Romans 8:18-23; Revelation 20:7-21:8 (NIV).

4. For further study about the new creation see Ross, *Beyond the Cosmos*, 217-228.

Further Resources

Journey Toward Creation. 2nd ed. Multilingual 70 min. Reasons To Believe in association with Global Net Productions. DVD. 2003.

Poe, Harry Lee, and J. Stanley Mattson, eds. *What God Knows: Time, Eternity, and Divine Knowledge*. Waco, TX: Baylor University Press, 2005.

Ross, Hugh. *Beyond the Cosmos: The Extra-Dimensionality of God; What Recent Discoveries in Astrophysics Reveal about the Glory and Love of God*. 2nd ed. Colorado Springs, CO: NavPress, 1999.

Glossary
of Science and Theology Terms

Agnosticism: (Gk. *a* - no, *gnosis* - knowledge) Literally: "no-knowledge-ism." The view that one does not, or can not, know ultimate reality (especially God). The position that God's existence cannot be determined due to an insufficiency of knowledge (thus implying the suspension of judgment).

Anthropic Principle: The observation that the universe has all the necessary and narrowly defined characteristics to make man and his sustained existence possible. The view that the universe is conspicuously "fine-tuned" for human existence.

Apologetics: (Gk. *apologia* - defense) The branch of Christian theology that provides rational justification for the truth claims of Christianity. Christian apologetics involves providing positive evidence for the faith, answering questions or objections, as well as critiquing alternative (non-Christian) systems of thought.

Atheism: (Gk. *a* - no, *theos* - God) Literally: "no-God-ism." The view that no God or gods exist. The position that denies or rejects the existence God.

Atonement: Satisfaction for wrongdoing or debt. In Christianity, the saving work of Jesus Christ on the cross (specifically His death) by which sinful human beings are restored to fellowship with their holy and just God.

Big Bang: The theory that the universe expands adiabatically according to the standard equations of general relativity from an initial state of infinite density, temperature, and pressure.

Cosmological Argument: One of the traditional proofs for the existence of God. Derived from the word "cosmos" (world), the argument attempts to prove that the world requires the existence of God as its ultimate cause.

Creatio Ex Nihilo: (Lat. phrase) Literally, "creation out of nothing." St. Augustine was the first to formulate the view that God created the world out of nothing (without the use of preexisting matter). The world was created purely by the creative power of God.

Deism: Belief in a God who created the world, but does not intervene within it (God is transcendent but not immanent). This religious worldview, which emphasizes natural law over revelation, was most popular during the seventeenth and eighteenth centuries in England, France, and America.

Determinism: The view that everything in the universe is controlled by previous conditions, and therefore could not be otherwise.

Empiricism: (Gk. *empeiria* - "experience") The view that all knowledge is acquired through five sense experience.

Entropy: A measure of the amount of energy in a disordered form (i.e., unavailable for work) within a system.

Epistemology: (Gk. *episteme* - "knowledge") The branch of philosophy concerned with the origin, nature, limits, and validity of knowledge.

Evolution, Theistic: The view that God's purposes are carried out through the normal evolutionary processes found in the natural world.

Foreknowledge, Divine: God's perfect knowledge of all actual and possible events.

Frame of Reference: The position in time and space from which measurements and observations are made.

Free Will: The view that human choices and actions are self-caused (i.e., uncoerced or independent of external causal factors).

General Revelation: God's expression of Himself to man through the realm of nature (apart from special revelation).

Grace: (Gk. *charis* - "favor" or "goodness") Biblically speaking, the unmerited favor of God. The goodness and kindness of God which is extended to undeserving mankind.

Humanism: The view that "mankind is the measure of all things." To invest mankind with supreme value.

Imago Dei: (Lat. "Image of God") Mankind was created in the image and likeness of God (Gen. 1:26-27). Though tarnished by the fall, mankind reflects the image of God in the following respects: personality, rationality, volition, and spirituality.

Incarnation: (Lat. *carne* - "flesh") Literally, "becoming in flesh." The Christian doctrine that Jesus Christ, the Second person of the Trinity, took to Himself a human nature and became man, without in any way diminishing His deity (John 1:1,14). Jesus Christ is one person with two distinguishable natures (divine and human).

Inerrancy: Literally, "without error." In its strongest form, a reference to the Bible being completely trustworthy in all matters in which it speaks (including matters of faith, practice, history, and science). The belief that the Bible, as a consequence of its divine inspiration, contains no contradictions or errors in its original autographs.

Inspiration: Biblically speaking, the process by which God moved the biblical writers to produce the scriptural books. This divine supervision removed the possibility of human error, but allowed the personality and style of the various writers to be reflected. Thus the Scriptures are *theopneustos* "God-breathed" (2 Tim. 3:16).

Light Year: The distance light travels in one year (approximately 5.9 trillion miles or 9.5 trillion kilometers).

Logic: The branch of philosophy concerned with the principles of correct reasoning. The science that evaluates thinking and argumentation.

Macroevolution: Evolution on a large or broad scale (change throughout the phylum).

Materialism: The metaphysical view that all reality is reducible to, or explainable in terms of, matter and its physical properties.

Microevolution: Evolution on a small or limited scale (change within species).

Microwave Background: The radiation left over from the big bang. This radiation follows the spectrum of a black body radiator with a temperature of about 3° Kelvin.

Miracle: A divine intervention into the natural order of affairs (inexplicable from a purely naturalistic viewpoint).

Naturalism: The view that the natural, material, and physical universe is the only reality. The philosophy of naturalism is characterized by monism, materialism, antisupernaturalism, scientism, and humanism.

Non-Contradiction, Law of: (A cannot equal A and non-A) One of the fundamental laws of logic. Stated metaphysically: "Something cannot both be and not be at the same time and in the same respect." Stated epistemologically: "Two contradictory statements cannot both be true at the same time and in the same respect."

Original Sin: The doctrine that the universal sinfulness of humanity (both guilt and moral corruption) came from Adam's initial sin (Gen. 3). The sinful condition of humanity was inherited from Adam.

Pantheism: (Gk. *pan* - "all" or "every," *theos* - "God") Literally, "all-God-ism." The view that makes God identical with the world. "All is God and God is all." The world and God are synonymous.

Polytheism: (Gk. *polus* - "much" or "many," *theos* - "God") Literally, "many-gods-ism." The belief in many (more than one) gods or deities.

Predestination: To foreordain. The sovereign decision and decree of God to determine the destiny of all souls. God's eternal selection of certain individuals for salvation (election).

Relativity, Special: A physical theory derived from the combined propositions that 1) there is no observable absolute motion, only relative motion, and 2) the velocity of light is constant and independent of the motion of the source.

Relativity, General: An extension of special relativity theory to include the effects of gravity on matter, energy, space, and time.

Revelation, General: Revelation of God made available to all people through the created order.

Revelation, Special: Revelation of God through a special source (Moses, Jesus Christ, the Bible).

Scientific Method: A method of empirical inquiry involving prediction, observation, and experimentation (a framework of restraint).

Singularity: An infinitely shrunken space representing the boundary at which space ceases to exist or at which space comes into existence.

Sovereignty of God: The view that makes God the absolute ruler and controller of all things. A reference to the absolute authority of God.

Special Creation: The doctrine that God personally intervened in the natural order to produce things that did not previously exist and that could not be produced by natural processes alone.

Supernova: The cataclysmic explosion of a massive star in which most of the star is blown off into interstellar space.

Teleological Argument: (Gk. *teleos* - "end" or "purpose") A proof for the existence of God. The argument stated: Design requires a designer. The universe exhibits evidence of complex design. Therefore, the universe was designed by a cosmic architect (God).

Theism: (From Gk. *theos* - "God") The worldview that affirms the existence of an infinite, eternal, and personal God, who is the transcendent creator, and immanent sustainer of the world. Judaism, Christianity, and Islam are considered theistic religions.

Transcendence of God: God being beyond, independent of, or distinct from, the time-space world.

Worldview: A conceptual framework for interpreting reality. An attempt to arrange one's most basic beliefs into a coherent system that can serve to evaluate and interpret reality. A comprehensive outlook on life.

Scholar Biographies

Hugh Ross

Hugh Ross is the founder and president of Reasons To Believe (RTB). This nonprofit and interdenominational think-tank provides research and teaching on the harmony of God's revelation in the Bible with His creative expression in the facts of nature. With grants from the National Research Council of Canada, Dr. Ross earned a B.Sc. in physics from the University of British Columbia and a Ph.D. in astronomy from the University of Toronto. For several years he continued his research on quasars and galaxies as a postdoctoral fellow at the California Institute of Technology (Caltech).

Kenneth Richard Samples

An experienced educator and author, **Kenneth Richard Samples** holds degrees in philosophy, social science, and theological studies. He has taught many courses at the college level and currently lectures for the Master of Arts program in Christian Apologetics at Biola University and at Providence Christian College. Kenneth also teaches adult classes at Christ Reformed Church in Southern California. Before joining the RTB scholar team, Kenneth worked as Senior Research Consultant and Correspondence Editor at the Christian Research Institute (CRI). While there he was a regular co-host of the popular call-in radio program "The Bible Answer Man" with Dr. Walter Martin.

David Rogstad

David Rogstad, a founding board member and scholar with RTB, earned a Ph.D. in physics from Caltech and continued his research in radio astronomy there. Later he worked as a team leader on many high-profile projects at Caltech's Jet Propulsion Laboratory (JPL). Dave loves studying and teaching from the Bible, and his specialty is communicating complex ideas, both scientific and spiritual, in simple terms that people can understand and apply.

Jeffrey Zweerink

Jeffrey Zweerink came to Reasons To Believe from the University of California at Los Angeles (UCLA) where he still works part-time on the physics and astronomy research faculty. He has co-authored more than 30 journal articles and numerous conference proceedings. Jeff's fascination with gamma rays developed during his graduate studies at Iowa State University, where he earned a Ph.D. in astronomy in 1997. As a Christian, Jeff's former struggles with science-and-faith issues gave him a passionate desire to explain how they integrate.

About Reasons To Believe

Founded in 1986, Reasons To Believe is an international, interdenominational ministry established to communicate the uniquely factual basis for belief in the Bible as the error-free Word of God and for personal faith in Jesus Christ as Creator and Savior.

Many people assume that science and faith are at odds with one another. The common conclusion is that we must either choose between them or keep them apart.

The mission of Reasons To Believe is to show that science and faith are, and always will be, allies—not enemies. Our mission is to bring that life-changing truth to as many people as possible.

It is our conviction that because the same God who "authored" the universe also inspired the writings of the Bible, a consistent message will come through both channels. In other words, the facts of nature will never contradict the words of the Bible when both are conscientiously interpreted.

We want to help unbelievers find answers to those questions that bar them from entrusting their lives to Christ. And we want to help Christians find new joy and confidence in worshiping the Creator as they shed their fear of science.

So, whether you are a skeptical inquirer, a new Christian, or one who has enjoyed a long relationship with the Lord, we look forward to providing you with resources that will keep you informed about up-to-the-minute scientific discoveries and how they harmonize with God's revelation in the words of the Bible.

REASONS
TO BELIEVE

P.O. Box 5978 ▪ Pasadena, CA 91117
(800) 482-7836 ▪ www.reasons.org

☎ RTB Hotline ☎
Daily ▪ 5:00–7:00 P.M. Pacific Time ▪ (626) 335-5282